Mystery Mob
and the Night
in the Waxworks

Roger Hurn

Illustrated by
Stik

RISING★STARS

Rising Stars UK Ltd.
22 Grafton Street, London W1S 4EX
www.risingstars-uk.com

The right of Roger Hurn to be identified as the author of this work
has been asserted by him in accordance with the Copyright,
Design and Patents Act 1988.

Published 2008

Cover design: Burville-Riley Partnership
Illustrator: Stik, Bill Greenhead for Illustration Ltd
Text design and typesetting: Andy Wilson
Publisher: Gill Budgell
Editor: Catherine Baker

British Library Cataloguing in Publication Data.
A CIP record for this book is available from the British Library

ISBN: 978-1-84680-430-4

Printed in the UK by CPI Bookmarque, Croydon, CR0 4TD

Mixed Sources
Product group from well-managed
forests and other controlled sources
www.fsc.org Cert no. TT-COC-002227
© 1996 Forest Stewardship Council

Contents

Meet the Mystery Mob

Name:

Gummy

FYI: Gummy hasn't got much brain – and even fewer teeth.

Loves: Soup.

Hates: Toffee chews.

Fact: The brightest thing about him is his shirt.

Name:

Lee

FYI: If Lee was any cooler he'd be a cucumber.

Loves: Hip-hop.

Hates: Hopscotch.

Fact: He has his own designer label (which he peeled off a tin).

Name:

FYI: Rob lives in his own world – he's just visiting planet Earth.

Loves: Daydreaming.

Hates: Nightmares.

Fact: Rob always does his homework – he just forgets to write it down.

Name:

Dwayne

FYI: Dwayne is smarter than a tree full of owls.

Loves: Anything complicated.

Hates: Join-the-dots books.

Fact: If he was any brighter you could use him as a floodlight at football matches.

Name:

Chet

FYI: Chet is as brave as a lion with steel jaws.

Loves: Having adventures.

Hates: Knitting.

Fact: He's as tough as the chicken his granny cooks for his tea.

Name:

Adi

FYI: Adi is as happy as a football fan with tickets to the big match.

Loves: Telling jokes.

Hates: Moaning minnies.

Fact: He knows more jokes than a jumbo joke book.

Charity Challenge

Rob and Lee are in Wendel's Weird Waxworks. They're going to spend the night in the Chamber of Horrors!

Rob   Why did you say we'd do this, Lee?

Lee   Because we'll raise loads of money for charity.

Rob   (gulping) But this waxworks is meant to be haunted!

Lee   Well, we'll soon find out if it is or it isn't.

Rob   Oooh, I wish we'd done
what Gummy did to raise money.

Lee   What! A sponsored
sweet sucking? I don't think so.
I like my teeth too much.

Rob   Okay, but Chet had a good idea.

Lee   Yeah, sponsored press-ups –
only you can't do them.

Rob   It's not my fault.
My arms go up all right.

Lee   Yeah, but your tummy and legs won't leave the ground.

Rob   I can't help it if they're afraid of heights.

Lee   Whatever.

Rob   Well, we could've told jokes like Adi.

Lee   Rob, your idea of a funny joke is 'What has two humps and is found at the North Pole?'

Rob	A lost camel! Hee! Hee! That makes me laugh.
Lee	Yeah, but it doesn't make anyone else laugh, so that's why we're not doing sponsored joke telling.
Rob	We could've done sponsored spelling like Dwayne.
Lee	Okay, then, spell *Rob*.
Rob	Yikes, why do you have to start with a hard one?

Lee   So sponsored spelling is out.
No, we'll make more money
for charity than the rest
of the Mystery Mob put together
if we can stay in here all night.

Rob   But no one's ever managed
it before. It's way too scary.

Lee   Well, *I'm* not afraid of a bunch
of waxwork models.

Rob   Nor am I – as long as they
            don't come to life in the middle
            of the night!

Wendel, the owner of the Waxworks,
comes in to see how the boys are doing.

Wendel Okay, guys. This is it. I'm off
            home now. Will you two
            be all right?

Lee   We'll be fine.

Rob   Will you be locking us in?

Wendel   No – if you get too scared,
you can just walk out
of the front door.

Lee   We won't.

Wendel   Hmm … you might not be
so brave when the lights go out.
Anyway, I'll see you
in the morning – I hope.

Wendel leaves.

Rob   What did he mean –
when the lights go out?

Lee   The lights are on a time switch.
They go off at midnight.

Rob   (shouting) Wendel, come back!
I want to go home.

Lee   Forget it, Rob. He's gone.
From now on it's just you,
me and the waxwork models!

Things That Go Bump in the Night

Rob and Lee settle down in their
sleeping bags, but they don't go to sleep.
Even with the lights on, the Waxworks
is a creepy place.

Rob   I'm going to try to sleep
with one eye open.

Lee   Why?

Rob   So I can see if any of the models
come to life in the night.

Lee   That won't happen.

Rob   What won't? Me sleeping
with one eye open?

Lee   No, the models coming to life.
They're made of wax.

Rob   But they look so alive.

Lee   The model of the Headless
Horseman doesn't.

Rob   Why not?

Lee   Duh! 'Cos he hasn't got a head.

Rob   Poor bloke. I feel sorry for him.

Lee   Yeah, but at least he never gets a headache!

Rob doesn't smile. Instead his eyes open wide in fright.

Rob   Ssshhhh! I can hear something.

Lee   Yeah, it's your teeth chattering.

Rob   No, it's not. Listen!

The two boys hear ghostly moans
coming from the next room.

Lee   It's probably just the wind.

Rob   Well, it's sure putting
           the wind up me.

Lee   Come on, let's go
           and investigate.

Rob   No way. I'm out of here.

MADDY
the moaning monster

Lee	If you go, we won't raise any money for charity.
Rob	But if I stay, I'll be *raising* the hairs on the back of my neck.
Lee	Oh, don't be such a chicken.
Rob	All right. But my mum likes me being a chicken.
Lee	What! Why's that?

19

Rob   It saves her buying eggs
from the shop.

Lee   Doh!

The boys tiptoe over to the next room.
Just as they are about to go inside,
the lights go out!

The Midnight Hour

Rob   Argggh! It's gone dark!

Lee   Quick, switch on your torch.

Rob   I have, and I still can't
see anything.

Lee   That's 'cos you've got
your eyes closed, you dummy!

Rob   (opening his eyes) Ah, right,
that's better.

Lee   It is if you like looking at
            a bunch of creepy monsters.

Rob   I don't, but at least they're
            in the shadows.

Lee   Yeah, those shadows make it easy
            for them to sneak up on us.

Rob   I thought you said
            they wouldn't do that.

Lee   That was before I heard
            that moaning noise.

Rob   So do you think one of these
            models is making it?

Lee   Maybe. Let's check them out. Shine your torch in each monster's face in turn.

Rob   Okay. First up it's Snackula, the vampire who's always peckish.

Lee   It's not him. He's not making any sound.

Rob   Phew. That's good. A hungry vampire's just a pain in the neck.

Lee   True. Now shine the light on Gilda Ghoul and her two demon mates.

Rob   Why does Gilda hang out
with demons?

Lee   'Cos demons are a ghoul's
best friend.

Rob   Er ... isn't it *diamonds* are
a *girl's* best friend?

Lee   Not in Gilda's case.

Rob   Fair enough. But it's not them.
They're not moving.

Lee   Which monster is it then?

Rob   Oh no. It's Maddy the Moaning
Monster. Look! She's the one
the sound's coming from!

Rob shines the torch beam on Maddy.

Lee   Hang on. The noise is coming
from Maddy all right, but her lips
aren't moving.

Rob   No, but my legs are. I'm gone.

Lee   Wait up, Rob. We're going
to take a closer look.

Rob and Lee go up to the waxwork
model. They see a small box behind it.

Rob   What's that?

Lee   It's a CD player, and it's making
the moaning sounds –
not Maddy.

Rob   So, someone's trying to scare us
            into leaving the Waxworks –
            but why?

Lee   I don't know.

Suddenly they hear the sound of a horse
galloping off down the corridor.

Rob   It's the Headless Horseman!

Trick, But No Treat

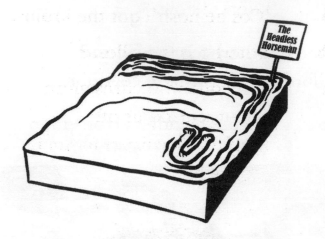

The boys dash back into the other room.
The model of the Headless Horseman
is gone.

Lee   I don't believe it!

Rob   No, listen, it all makes sense.
The Headless Horseman wants us
out. He used the CD player
to do the moaning 'cos he hasn't
got a head.

Lee   The Headless Horseman
          isn't behind this.

Rob   How do you know?

Lee   'Cos he hasn't got the brains.

Rob   But who is the villain?

Lee   Someone who cares more
          about scaring us off
          than about raising money
          for charity.

Rob   Okay, but have you got any idea who that is?

Lee   I'm not sure, but let's set a trap and see who falls into it.

Rob   How are we going to do that?

Lee   First up, we're going to slam the front door.

Rob   Why?

Lee   'Cos that'll make the bad guy think we've run off home.

Rob   Gotcha!

Lee   Then we'll tie a piece of string across the entrance to the Chamber of Horrors. The bad guy will never see it in the dark.

Rob   So he'll trip over our trip wire?

Lee   Exactly.

Rob   But what if it's someone really scary?

Lee   Don't worry. He'll be the one being scared.

Rob   How come?

Lee   Remember Gilda the Ghoul's two demon mates?

Rob   Yeah, they're horrible!

Lee   They are. Well, we're going to hide them. Then we'll dress up in their outfits and take their place next to Gilda. When the bad guy falls over we'll leap out on him.

Rob   But won't he see it's us?

Lee   Not with all the lights out. All he'll see are two screaming demons jumping up and down on him.

Rob   I like it!

The Night Tripper

The boys slam the front door, then set up the trip wire. They dress up in the demon costumes. Then they go and stand next to Gilda.

Rob   I don't like Gilda.
          She's well creepy.

Lee   Oh, I don't know. She seems
          like a nice ghoul to me.

Rob   Doh!

The boys hear footsteps outside in the corridor.

Lee   (whispering) Sssshhhh.
            I can hear someone coming.

Rob   Please don't let it be
            the headless horseman.

A shadowy figure appears. It trips over
the string and falls flat on its face.
Rob and Lee jump on top of it.
They scream at the tops of their voices.

Man   Argggh! Help! I'm being
            attacked by demons!

Lee   Shine the torch in his face, Rob!
Let's see who it is.

Rob   Well, if he's got a face
at least it can't be
the Headless Horseman.

He switches on his torch.

Lee   It's Wendel!

Wendel Please stop jumping on me, guys.
I give up!

Rob   Okay, but why did you try
to scare us off?

Wendel Because if you told people
my Waxworks is haunted,
then everyone would come
to see it and I'd be rich.

Lee But what about our sponsor
money? You didn't care
about that, did you?

Wendel You're right. Look, how about
I write you a cheque for £100
for your charity. Will that
make up for things?

Rob   That sounds fair – as long
as we can still stay here all night.
If we don't, we can't collect
our sponsor money.

Wendel That's fine by me.

Lee   Great. Then tomorrow
we'll tell all our sponsors
that your Chamber of Horrors
is really ghoul!

About the author

Roger Hurn has:

- had a hit record in Turkey
- won *The Weakest Link* on TV
- swum with sharks on the Great Barrier Reef.

Now he's a writer, and he hopes you like reading about the Mystery Mob as much as he likes writing about them.

Waxworks quiz

Questions

1 How do you make a waxworks dummy?

2 Why don't they use heaters in
the wax museum?

3 Why did the waxworks attendant say
the model of Skippy the Kangaroo
was out of bounds?

4 What came after the model of the T-Rex
in the waxworks?

5 What waxworks model runs
but never walks?

6 What kind of model did the waxworks
make when they mixed up
a Scottish legend and a rotten egg?

7 The waxworks made a model of a cake
that wanted to rule the world.
Who was it?

8 Why is the Chamber of Horrors so noisy?

Answers

1 You use clay, a mould and hot wax – and stop calling me dummy!
2 They don't want the dummies to melt!
3 Because it was really tired!
4 Its tail!
5 One that's melting!
6 The Loch Ness Pongster!
7 Attila the Bun!
8 Because of the coffin!

How did you score?

✋ If you got all eight waxworks answers correct, then you are definitely not a dummy!

✋ If you got six waxworks answers correct, then you are a model quizzer!

✋ If you got fewer than four waxworks answers correct, then you're going into meltdown!

When I was a kid

Question Did you ever go to a waxworks museum when you were a kid?

Roger No, because the waxworks made fun of my local football team.

Question How did they do that?

Roger Well, the manager asked the waxworks to make him a team of 11 dummies. He wanted our players to practise moves against them in training.

Question So what happened?

Roger The wax dummies beat my team 3-1!

Question Gosh. Your favourite team must have been pretty bad!

Roger No, they weren't. The waxworks made dummies of the world's top players. My team didn't stand a chance!

Adi's favourite waxworks museum joke

Who's the scariest fish in the Chamber of Horrors?

Jack the Kipper!

Five fantastic facts about waxworks museums

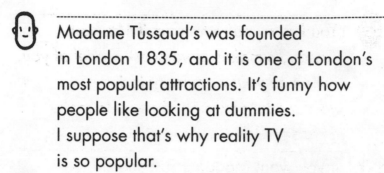

Madame Tussaud's was founded in London 1835, and it is one of London's most popular attractions. It's funny how people like looking at dummies. I suppose that's why reality TV is so popular.

Before coming to London, Madame Tussaud lived in France and spent her time during the French Revolution making death masks of those who were guillotined. Nice!

The most popular part of Madame Tussaud's is the Chamber of Horrors. It's a really creepy place. In fact, it's a bit like your school when the kids have gone home, but the teachers are still there.

*You know you're famous if Madame
Tussaud's makes a waxwork model of you.
But when your popularity fades,
your model gets melted down to make
a model of the next big star.*

If you want Madame Tussaud's
to make a waxwork model of you,
the good news is that they'll do it.
The bad news is that it'll cost you
£150,000!

How to enjoy a trip to a waxworks museum

1 Keep moving, otherwise people may think you're one of the dummies!

2 Don't try and stay the night in the Chamber of Horrors – you'll scare the monsters!

3 Don't walk around saying in a loud voice that none of the models look very lifelike. The attendants hate that – and so do the dummies!

4 Don't be like the person who said the famous sports star's model looked really ugly – only to find that it WAS the famous sports star. He was visiting the museum!

5 Don't say the models of the wives of Henry the Eighth don't look very happy – have you seen the model of Henry the Eighth?

Waxworks lingo

Exhibition The name given to a display of waxworks models. If you go to see the waxworks – do try not to make an exhibition of yourself!

Alginate Dentists use this stuff to make moulds of your teeth. Waxworks sculptors use it to make the waxwork models' hands.

Glass fibre The waxworks models' bodies are made of glass fibre.

Sculptor The person who makes the waxwork model's head. They use clay – not wax.

Mould A plaster mould goes round the clay head of the model. It's then removed to make a hollow plaster shell.

Molten wax Very hot wax that is poured into the mould. When it cools, the mould is removed to reveal a hollow wax head. Scary!

Mystery Mob

Mystery Mob Set 1:

Mystery Mob and the Abominable Snowman
Mystery Mob and the Big Match
Mystery Mob and the Circus of Doom
Mystery Mob and the Creepy Castle
Mystery Mob and the Haunted Attic
Mystery Mob and the Hidden Treasure
Mystery Mob and the Magic Bottle
Mystery Mob and the Missing Millions
Mystery Mob and the Monster on the Moor
Mystery Mob and the Mummy's Curse
Mystery Mob and the Time Machine
Mystery Mob and the UFO

Mystery Mob Set 2:

Mystery Mob and the Ghost Town
Mystery Mob and the Bonfire Night Plot
Mystery Mob and the April Fools' Day Joker
Mystery Mob and the Great Pancake Day Race
Mystery Mob and the Scary Santa
Mystery Mob and the Conker Conspiracy
Mystery Mob and the Top Talent Contest
Mystery Mob and the Night in the Waxworks
Mystery Mob and the Runaway Train
Mystery Mob and the Wrong Robot
Mystery Mob and the Day of the Dinosaurs
Mystery Mob and the Man-eating Tiger

RISING STARS

Mystery Mob books are available from most booksellers.

**For mail order information
please call Rising Stars on 0871 47 23 010
or visit www.risingstars-uk.com**